2 Describe fully each of the numbered and bracketed melodic intervals (e.g. major

J. S. Bach, Sonata for t

etc.

Intervals:

1 ....

2 ....

3 ....

4 ....

5 ....

3 The following melody is written for clarinet in B♭. Transpose it *down* a major 2nd, as it will sound at concert pitch. Do *not* use a key signature but remember to put in all necessary sharp, flat or natural signs.

Gal, Clarinet Sonata, Op. 84

etc.

4 Look at this extract from a piano sonatina by A. Diabelli and then answer the questions that follow.

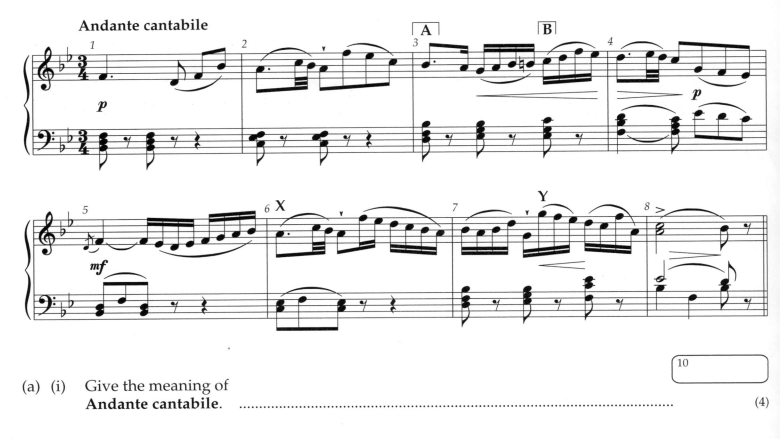

(a) (i) Give the meaning of
Andante cantabile. .... (4)

(ii) Draw a circle around *four successive* notes that form part of a chromatic scale. (2)

(iii) Rewrite the first two right-hand notes of the extract so that they sound at the same
pitch, but using the tenor C clef. Remember to put in the clef and the key signature.

(4)

Music Theory Past Papers 2012

ABRSM Grade 5

Theory Paper Grade 5 2012 A

Duration 2 hours

TOTAL MARKS
100

This paper contains SEVEN questions, ALL of which should be answered.
Write your answers on this paper – no others will be accepted.
Answers must be written clearly and neatly – otherwise marks may be lost.

1 (a) Look at the following extract and then answer the questions below.

15

Berg, String Quartet, Op. 3

etc.

(i) The extract begins on the first beat of the bar. Put in the time signature at the beginning
and add the missing bar-lines. The first bar-line is given. (5)

(ii) Complete the following statement:

The sextuplet ( ) means
six demisemiquavers (32nd notes) in the time of .... (2)

(b) Look at the following extract and then answer the questions below.

Moderato

Haydn, Piano Sonata in C♯ minor, Hob. XVI/36

etc.

(i) Rewrite the first left-hand chord of the extract so that it sounds at the same pitch, but using
the alto C clef. Remember to put in the clef and the key signature.

(4)

(ii) Give the meaning of *ten.* (short for *tenuto*) (bar 4). .... (2)

(iii) Write as a breve (double whole-note) an enharmonic equivalent of the first right-hand note
of bar 3.

(2)

(b) (i) Describe the chords in bar 3 marked [A] and [B] as I, II, IV or V. Also indicate ⬚10
whether the lowest note of the chord is the root (a), 3rd (b) or 5th (c).
The key is B♭ major.

Chord **A** .... Chord **B** .... (4)

(ii) Below the staves write Ic–V ($^6_4$ $^5_3$) under the *two successive* chords in bars 1– 4 where this
progression occurs. (2)

(iii) Give the technical names (e.g. tonic, dominant) of the two notes in the right-hand part
marked **X** and **Y**. Remember that the key is B♭ major.

X (bar 6) .... (2)

Y (bar 7) .... (2)

⬚10

(c) (i) Which other key has the same key signature as B♭ major? .... (2)

(ii) Name two standard orchestral instruments, one string and one woodwind, that
could play the right-hand part of bars 1–4 so that it sounds at the same pitch.

String .... (2)

Woodwind .... (2)

(iii) Name two standard orchestral percussion instruments, one (other than the piano) that
produces notes of definite pitch and one that produces notes of indefinite pitch.

Definite pitch .... (2)

Indefinite pitch .... (2)

5 (a) Write the key signature of five sharps and then one octave **descending** of the **melodic** minor scale with that key signature. Use semibreves (whole notes), begin on the tonic and remember to put in any necessary additional sharp, flat or natural signs. [10]

(b) Using semibreves (whole notes), write one octave **ascending** of the major scale that begins on the given note. Do *not* use a key signature but put in all necessary sharp or flat signs.

6 EITHER

(a) Compose a complete melody for unaccompanied flute or violin, using the given opening. **Indicate the tempo and other performance directions**, including any that might be particularly required for the instrument chosen. The complete melody should be eight bars long.

Instrument for which the melody is written: ....

OR

(b) Compose a complete melody to the following words for a solo voice. Write each syllable under the note or notes to which it is to be sung. Also **indicate the tempo and other performance directions as appropriate**.

> It is, it is a glorious thing
> To be a Pirate King!   *W. S. Gilbert*

7 Suggest suitable progressions for two cadences in the following melody by indicating ONLY ONE chord (I, II, IV or V) at each of the places marked A–E. You do not have to indicate the position of the chords, or to state which note is in the bass.

Show the chords:

EITHER (a) by writing I, II etc. or any other recognized symbols on the dotted lines below;

OR (b) by writing notes on the staves.

FIRST CADENCE:

Chord A ....

Chord B ....

SECOND CADENCE:

Chord C ....

Chord D ....

Chord E ....

BLANK PAGE

Theory Paper Grade 5   2012   B

Duration 2 hours

TOTAL MARKS
100

This paper contains SEVEN questions, ALL of which should be answered.
Write your answers on this paper – no others will be accepted.
Answers must be written clearly and neatly – otherwise marks may be lost.

1 (a) The following extract begins on the first beat of the bar. Put in the missing bar-lines.

15

Mozart, Piano Sonata in C minor, K. 457

etc. (3)

(b) Look at the following extract and then answer the questions below.

Haydn, Piano Sonata in B♭, Hob. XVI/18

etc.

(i) Describe the chords marked ⌐A⌐ and ⌐B⌐ as I, II, IV or V. Also indicate whether the lowest note of the chord is the root (a), 3rd (b) or 5th (c). The key is B♭ major.

Chord **A** (bar 3) ....   (2)

Chord **B** (bar 5) ....   (2)

(ii) Name each of the ornaments in the right-hand part of bars 1 and 3.

Bar 1 ....   (2)

Bar 3 ....   (2)

(iii) Give the technical names (e.g. tonic, dominant) of the two notes in the right-hand part marked **X** and **Y**. Remember that the key is B♭ major.

X (bar 4) ....   (2)

Y (bar 5) ....   (2)

2 This passage is for SATB choir, written in short score. Rewrite it in open score.

Palestrina, *Missa Aeterna Christi munera* (adapted)

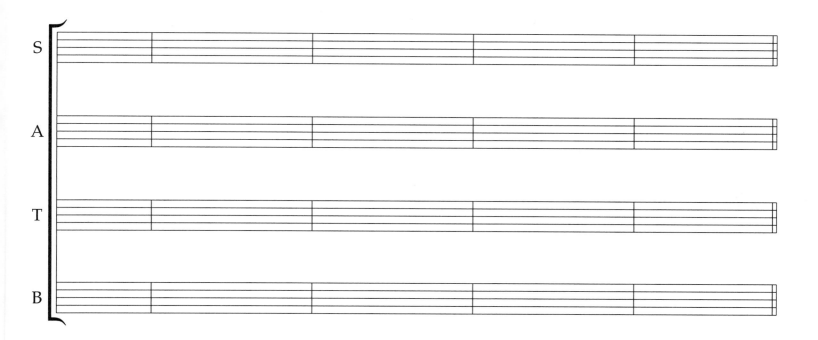

3 Look at this extract, which is from *Nocturne* for flute and piano by Michael Rose, and then answer the questions that follow.

10

(a) (i) Give the meaning of:

molto sostenuto ed espressivo .... (4)

P .... (2)

(ii) Rewrite the first two left-hand piano notes of the extract so that they sound at the same pitch, but using the tenor C clef. Remember to put in the clef and the key signature.

(4)

(b) (i) Give the letter name of the
highest note in the right-hand piano part.   ....   (2)

(ii) Describe fully each of the numbered and bracketed melodic intervals *in the left-hand piano part* (e.g. major 2nd).

1 (bar 7)   ....   (2)

2 (bar 7)   ....   (2)

3 (bars 7–8)   ....   (2)

(iii) Write as a breve (double whole-note) an enharmonic equivalent of the last flute note of the extract.

(2)

(c) (i) Rewrite the flute part of bar 2 in simple time but without changing the rhythmic effect. Remember to include the new time signature.

(4)

(ii) Complete the following statements:

The flute is a member of the .... family of orchestral instruments.   (2)

Another family of standard orchestral instruments is the .... family,   (2)

and its lowest-sounding member is the ....   (2)

13

4 (a) Put sharps or flats in front of the notes that need them to form the scale of D♭ major. Do *not* use a key signature.

(b) Write the key signature of four sharps and then one octave **ascending** of the **harmonic** minor scale with that key signature. Use semibreves (whole notes), begin on the tonic and remember to put in any necessary additional sharp, flat or natural signs.

5 The following melody is written for horn in F. Transpose it *down* a perfect 5th, as it will sound at concert pitch. Do *not* use a key signature but remember to put in all necessary sharp, flat or natural signs.

Schoenberg, Chamber Symphony No. 1

etc.

(a) Compose a complete melody for unaccompanied cello or bassoon, using the given opening. **Indicate the tempo and other performance directions**, including any that might be particularly required for the instrument chosen. The complete melody should be eight bars long.

Instrument for which the melody is written: ....

OR

(b) Compose a complete melody to the following words for a solo voice. Write each syllable under the note or notes to which it is to be sung. Also **indicate the tempo and other performance directions as appropriate**.

> This is the weather the cuckoo likes,
> And so do I. *Thomas Hardy*

7 Suggest suitable progressions for two cadences in the following melody by indicating ONLY ONE chord (I, II, IV or V) at each of the places marked A–E. You do not have to indicate the position of the chords, or to state which note is in the bass.

Show the chords:

EITHER   (a)   by writing I, II etc. or any other recognized symbols on the dotted lines below;

OR   (b)   by writing notes on the staves.

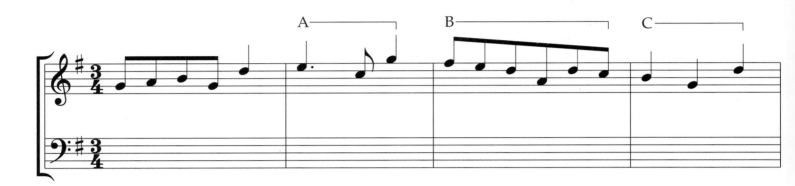

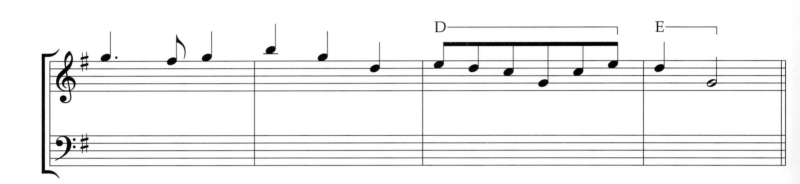

FIRST CADENCE:

Chord A   ....

Chord B   ....

Chord C   ....

SECOND CADENCE:

Chord D   ....

Chord E   ....

BLANK PAGE

Theory Paper Grade 5   2012   C

Duration 2 hours

This paper contains SEVEN questions, ALL of which should be answered.
Write your answers on this paper – no others will be accepted.
Answers must be written clearly and neatly – otherwise marks may be lost.

1 (a) The following extract, which begins on the first beat of the bar, contains some changes of time signature. Put in the correct time signature at each of the three places marked *.

Peter Maxwell Davies, *Apple Basket: Apple Blossom*

(6)

(b) Look at the following extract and then answer the questions below.

Mozart, Piano Sonata in B♭, K. 570 (adapted)

(i) Describe the chords marked ⌐X⌐, ⌐Y⌐ and ⌐Z⌐ as I, II, IV or V. Also indicate whether the lowest note of the chord is the root (a), 3rd (b) or 5th (c). The key is E♭ major.

Chord **X** .... (2)

Chord **Y** .... (2)

Chord **Z** .... (2)

(ii) Rewrite the first left-hand note of the extract so that it sounds at the same pitch, but using the alto C clef. Remember to put in the clef and the key signature.

(3)

18

2 Describe fully each of the numbered and bracketed melodic intervals (e.g. major 2nd).

Schoenberg, String Quartet No. 2, Op. 10

Intervals:

1 ....

2 ....

3 ....

4 ....

5 ....

3 These are the actual sounds made by a cor anglais. Rewrite the passage as it would appear for the player to read, that is, transpose it *up* a perfect 5th. Remember to put in the new key signature and add any necessary accidentals.

Skryabin, *Le poème de l'extase*

4 Look at this extract, which is adapted from a piece for violin and piano by Adam Carse, and then answer the questions that follow.

(a) (i) **Mark clearly on the music**, using the appropriate capital letter for identification, one example of each of the following. Also give the bar number of each of your answers, as shown in the answer to **A**.

    A an instruction to get gradually quieter.   Bar ......4......

    B in bars 1–4 of the violin part, a supertonic note
       in the key of D major (circle the note concerned).   Bar ....

         (2)

    C in bars 1–4 of the right-hand piano part, a note that
       is *not* in the key of D major (circle the note concerned).   Bar ....

         (2)

    D in bars 5–8 of the piano part, a note that is an
       enharmonic equivalent of E♭ (circle the note concerned).   Bar ....

         (2)

(ii) Rewrite the first right-hand piano chord of the extract so that it sounds at the same pitch, but using the tenor C clef. Remember to put in the clef and the key signature.

         (4)

(b) (i) Give the meaning of:

10

Andante grazioso .... (4)

⊓ (violin, bar 1) .... (2)

poco rit. (bar 8) .... (2)

(ii) Describe the time signature as:

simple or compound .... (1)

duple, triple or quadruple .... (1)

(c) (i) Answer TRUE or FALSE to each of the following:

10

The largest melodic interval in the violin part is a major 6th. .... (2)

All the notes in the left-hand piano part of
bars 5–7 can be found in the scale of E major. .... (2)

(ii) Complete the following statement:

The violin is the highest-sounding member of
the string family of orchestral instruments, and
the lowest-sounding member of this family is the .... (2)

(iii) Now name a *different* family of standard orchestral instruments and state its
highest-sounding member.

Family .... Instrument .... (4)

5 (a) Using semibreves (whole notes), write one octave **descending** of the major scale that begins on the given note. Do *not* use a key signature but put in all necessary sharp or flat signs.

(b) Write one octave **ascending** of the scale of F♯ **harmonic** minor. Do *not* use a key signature but put in all necessary sharp or flat signs. Use semibreves (whole notes) and begin on the tonic.

6 EITHER

(a) Compose a complete melody for unaccompanied flute or trumpet, using the given opening. **Indicate the tempo and other performance directions**, including any that might be particularly required for the instrument chosen. The complete melody should be eight bars long.

Instrument for which the melody is written: ....

OR

(b) Compose a complete melody to the following words for a solo voice. Write each syllable under the note or notes to which it is to be sung. Also **indicate the tempo and other performance directions as appropriate**.

> The wind was a torrent of darkness
> Among the gusty trees.
>
> *Alfred Noyes*

Reproduced by kind permission of The Society of Authors as the Literary Representative of the Estate of Alfred Noyes.

7 Suggest suitable progressions for two cadences in the following melody by indicating **ONLY ONE** chord (I, II, IV or V) at each of the places marked A–E. You do not have to indicate the position of the chords, or to state which note is in the bass.

10

Show the chords:

EITHER (a) by writing I, II etc. or any other recognized symbols on the dotted lines below;

OR (b) by writing notes on the staves.

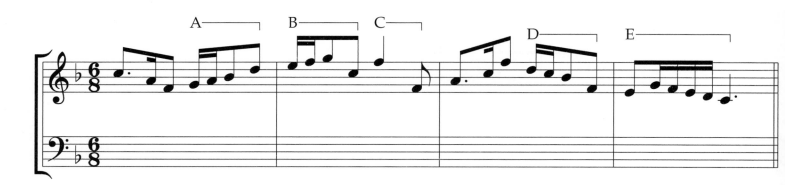

FIRST CADENCE: SECOND CADENCE:

Chord A   ....

                                                  Chord D   ....

Chord B   ....

                                                  Chord E   ....

Chord C   ....

BLANK PAGE

Theory Paper Grade 5   2012   S

Duration 2 hours

This paper contains SEVEN questions, ALL of which should be answered.
Write your answers on this paper – no others will be accepted.
Answers must be written clearly and neatly – otherwise marks may be lost.

TOTAL MARKS
100

1 (a) The following extract, which begins on the first beat of the bar, contains some
changes of time signature. Put in the correct time signature at each of the three
places marked ∗.

15

Stravinsky, *The Rite of Spring*

(6)

(b) Look at the following extract and then answer the questions below.

Andante un poco allegretto

Benda, Sonatina in G minor

etc.

(i) Draw a circle around *three successive* notes that form part of a chromatic scale. (2)

(ii) Describe the chords marked ⌈A⌉ and ⌈B⌉ as I, II, IV or V. Also indicate whether the lowest
note of the chord is the root (a), 3rd (b) or 5th (c). The key is G minor.

Chord **A** (bar 1) .... (2)

Chord **B** (bar 3) .... (2)

(iii) Rewrite the last left-hand note of the extract so that it sounds at the same pitch, but using
the alto C clef. Remember to put in the clef and the key signature.

(3)

2 Describe fully each of the numbered and bracketed melodic intervals (e.g. major 2nd).

J. S. Bach, Violin Sonata No. 3, BWV 1005

Intervals:

1 ....

2 ....

3 ....

4 ....

5 ....

3 The following melody is written for clarinet in B♭. Transpose it *down* a major 2nd, as it will sound at concert pitch. Remember to put in the new key signature and add any necessary accidentals.

Finzi, Fughetta

4 Look at this extract from a piece for bassoon and piano by Michael Rose, and then answer the questions that follow.

(a) (i) **Mark clearly on the music**, using the appropriate capital letter for identification, one example of each of the following. Also give the bar number of each of your answers, as shown in the answer to **A**.

   A in the bassoon part, a subdominant note in the key of C major (circle the note concerned).   Bar ....2....

   B in the bassoon part, a melodic interval of a diminished 5th (circle the notes concerned).   Bar ....   (2)

   C in the bassoon part, a sign that means to give slight emphasis to a note.   Bar ....   (2)

   D in the piano part, a chord of C minor in first inversion.   Bar ....   (2)

   (ii) Name one similarity and one difference *in the bassoon part* between bars 5 and 6.

   Similarity   ....   (1)

   Difference   ....   (1)

   (iii) Rewrite the last bassoon note of the extract so that it sounds at the same pitch, but using the tenor C clef. Remember to put in the clef sign.

   (2)

28

(b) (i) Give the meaning of:

Alla marcia .... (2)

$\downarrow = 100$ .... (2)

(ii) Rewrite the bassoon part of bar 4 in compound time but without changing the rhythmic effect. Remember to put in the new time signature.

(4)

(iii) Write as a breve (double whole-note) an enharmonic equivalent of the first bassoon note of the extract.

(2)

(c) (i) Answer TRUE or FALSE to each of the following statements:

The bassoon is a double-reed instrument. .... (2)

The bassoon is a transposing instrument. .... (2)

A bassoonist might be asked to play pizzicato. .... (2)

(ii) The bassoon is a member of the woodwind family of orchestral instruments. Name a standard orchestral instrument from a *different* family that could play the bassoon part of the extract so that it sounds at the same pitch, and state the family of instruments to which it belongs.

Instrument .... Family .... (4)

5 (a) Write the key signature of five sharps and then one octave **descending** of the major scale with that key signature. Use semibreves (whole notes) and begin on the tonic.

[10]

(b) Using semibreves (whole notes), write one octave **ascending** of the **melodic** minor scale that has the given key signature. Begin on the tonic and remember to put in any necessary additional sharp, flat or natural signs.

6 EITHER

(a) Compose a complete melody for unaccompanied trombone or cello, using the given opening. **Indicate the tempo and other performance directions**, including any that might be particularly required for the instrument chosen. The complete melody should be eight bars long.

Instrument for which the melody is written: ....

OR

(b) Compose a complete melody to the following words for a solo voice. Write each syllable under the note or notes to which it is to be sung. Also **indicate the tempo and other performance directions as appropriate**.

> Only the actions of the just
> Smell sweet, and blossom in their dust.   *James Shirley*

7 Suggest suitable progressions for two cadences in the following melody by indicating ONLY ONE chord (I, II, IV or V) at each of the places marked A–E. You do not have to indicate the position of the chords, or to state which note is in the bass.

Show the chords:

EITHER (a) by writing I, II etc. or any other recognized symbols on the dotted lines below;

OR (b) by writing notes on the staves.

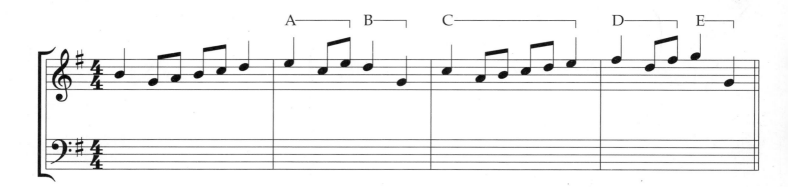

FIRST CADENCE:

Chord A ....

Chord B ....

SECOND CADENCE:

Chord C ....

Chord D ....

Chord E ....

Support material for ABRSM Theory exams

ABRSM
24 Portland Place
London W1B 1LU
United Kingdom

www.abrsm.org

ISBN 978-1-84849-452-7

MIX
Paper from responsible sources
FSC™ C109619

Published by ABRSM (Publishing) Ltd, a wholly owned subsidiary of ABRSM
Cover by Kate Benjamin & Andy Potts
Printed in England by Halstan & Co. Ltd, Amersham, Bucks
Reprinted in 2015